THE M

WHO PUSHED

MW00622629

ON 1ST JULY 1921 RISING STAR MOLLY MAY WAS HANDED THE OPPORTUNITY OF A LIFETIME; A LEAD ROLE IN THE WEST END MUSICAL 'THE LADY OF THE ROSE'.

REPLACING A HIT PLAY THAT HAD BEEN RUNNING FOR YEARS, THE PRESSURE WAS ON FOR MOLLY TO DELIVER TO THE LARGE CROWDS AND PAPARAZZI THAT HAD GATHERED ON THE OPENING NIGHT.

UNFORTUNATELY THE SHOW DID NOT GO TO PLAN..

PLAGUED BY EQUIPMENT FAILURES, FLUFFED LINES, AND STUMBLES, THE NIGHT WAS A DISASTER AND MOLLY'S BIG MOMENT HAD BEEN RUINED. LITTLE DID SHE KNOW THAT WORSE WAS YET TO COME!

STORMING OUT OF THE THEATRE, MOLLY APPEARED TO TRIP AS SHE FELL DOWN THE GRAND STAIRCASE, INSISTING THAT SHE'D BEEN PUSHED!

WAS SHE BETRAYED BY A JEALOUS CO-STAR OR THE VICTIM OF A BITTER LOVE RIVAL?

YOU MUST RETURN TO THE SCENE OF LONDON'S WEST END, UNCOVER THE HIDDEN CRYPTIC CLUES, AND FINALLY UNMASK THE ACTRESS BEHIND THE MOST LEGENDARY SHOWBIZ BETRAYAL!

THE CHARACTER OF MOLLY MAY AND THE STORIES RELATED TO HER THROUGHOUT THIS BOOK ARE ALL FICTIONAL, HOWEVER THE HISTORICAL INFORMATION AND ALL EXTRA DETAILS RELATED TO EACH CLUE ARE FACTUAL, AND BASED ON DETAILED HISTORICAL RESEARCH.

HOW TO PLAY

1

Follow the Maps
to find the location
of your clue

2

Solve the Clue to eliminate one
option from the list on page 1
(Extra help is on the back page)

3

At each stop you will
**Unravel more of
the legendary tale.**

4

At the end of your adventure your last
remaining items on Page 1 will
Reveal the final Secrets of the Mystery

IMPORTANT INFORMATION

1 On rare occasions, clues may be temporarily covered or permanently removed. In this instance we ask you to use the extra clues at the back of the book, and if possible, please report this to us.
It is recommended that you do the activity within 3 months of purchase, to reduce this risk.

2 Take care! You are responsible for yourself and your group. Be careful crossing roads, make sure to respect old monuments and private property, and if you are drinking alcohol please drink responsibly.

3 Any food & drink discounts available in this booklet are at the discretion of the stated premises, and may be subject to change or cancellation.

DIRECTIONS TO STARTING POINT:

THE STARTING POINT FOR THE TREASURE HUNT IS <u>INSIDE</u>

THE LAMB & FLAG PUB

33 ROSE STREET, COVENT GARDEN, LONDON. WC2E 9EB

⚠️ <u>PLEASE NOTE</u>: THE PUB OPENS AT 12PM

ONCE ENTERING THE PUB, YOU CAN BEGIN YOUR TREASURE HUNT WITH YOUR FIRST CLUE!

THE LAMB & FLAG

CLUE 1

(Your clue is inside the pub)

PLEASE NOTE: THE PUB OPENS AT 12PM

AN OLD BRASS PLATE ABOVE THE BAR,

HAS A NAME YOU NEED TO KNOW.

A MAN CALLED 'BOB' HOLDS THE CLUE,

TO ELIMINATE A SHOW.

ELIMINATE

ELIMINATE A SHOW FOUND IN HIS NAME.

(Extra help on back page)

THE LAMB & FLAG HAS BEEN A LICENCED PREMISES SINCE THE 17TH CENTURY, AND OVER THE YEARS HAS BEEN FREQUENTED BY A NUMBER OF FAMOUS FIGURES INCLUDING CHARLES DICKENS.

IN THE 19TH CENTURY THE UPSTAIRS ROOM WAS FAMOUS FOR HOSTING BAREKNUCKLE PRIZE FIGHTS, WHICH GAINED IT THE GORY NICKNAME OF 'BUCKET O' BLOOD' BOXING MEMORABILIA CAN BE SEEN ON DISPLAY THROUGHOUT THE BUILDING.

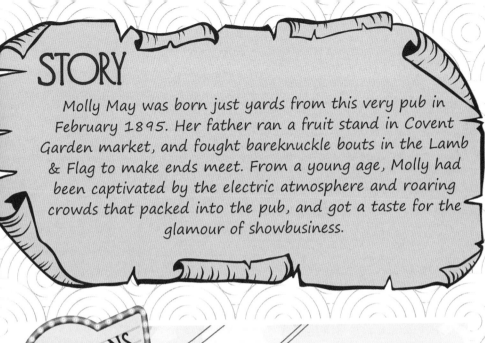

STORY

Molly May was born just yards from this very pub in February 1895. Her father ran a fruit stand in Covent Garden market, and fought bareknuckle bouts in the Lamb & Flag to make ends meet. From a young age, Molly had been captivated by the electric atmosphere and roaring crowds that packed into the pub, and got a taste for the glamour of showbusiness.

DIRECTIONS

ST. PAUL'S CHURCH

Rose Street · Floral Street · Garrick Street · King Street · New Row · Bedford Street · Henrietta Street · Maiden Lane

EXIT THE PUB AND HEAD STRAIGHT INTO GARRICK STREET.

TURN LEFT, AND THEN TAKE THE FIRST LEFT INTO KING STREET.

AT THE END OF THE STREET YOU WILL ENTER THE AREA OF COVENT GARDEN. LOOK FOR ST PAUL'S CHURCH, AND FIND A BLACK METAL PLAQUE ON THE OUTSIDE.

ST PAUL'S CHURCH WAS ONCE DESTROYED BY A
TERRIBLE FIRE, BUT REBUILT TO ITS FORMER GLORY.
WRITE THE DATE THAT THE CHURCH
REOPENED FOR SERVICE:

__ __ / __ __ / __ __ __ __

I = 1	XL = 40	C = 100	DC = 600
V = 5	L = 50	CC = 200	DCC = 700
X = 10	LX = 60	CCC = 300	DCCC = 800
XX = 20	LXXX = 80	CD = 400	CM = 900
XXX = 30	XC = 90	D = 500	M = 1000

ADD ALL OF THE SINGLE DIGITS OF THE DATE TOGETHER TO

ELIMINATE A NUMBER FROM YOUR LIST.

THE AREA OF COVENT GARDEN WAS ONCE A WALLED
GARDEN KNOWN AS 'THE GARDEN OF THE ABBEY AND
CONVENT' WHICH WAS MAINTAINED BY MONKS, PROVIDING
ORCHARDS AND ARABLE FARM LAND TO WESTMINSTER
ABBEY.

COVENT GARDEN TODAY IS SYNONYMOUS WITH STREET
PERFORMANCES, AND IT WAS HERE IN 1662 THAT THE
DIARIST SAMUEL PEPYS RECORDED THE FIRST EVER MENTION
OF THE FAMOUS 'PUNCH & JUDY' PUPPET SHOW.

STORY

Molly was christened in 'The Actors Church', but despite that, her parents had no desire for her to become an actress. Drama schools were expensive and the profession was considered too risky for vulnerable young women. However, as Molly spent most of her time growing up playing in the area of Covent Garden and watching the lively mix of street performances, she became convinced that the stage was her destiny.

DIRECTIONS

FROM ST PAUL'S CHURCH, HEAD THROUGH THE CENTRE OF COVENT GARDEN MARKET AND OUT THE OTHER SIDE.

ENTER RUSSELL STREET, THEN KEEP WALKING UNTIL YOU FIND THE THEATRE ROYAL.

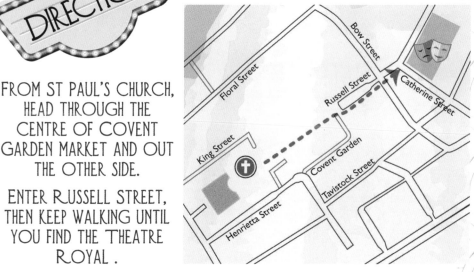

YOUR CLUE CAN BE FOUND ON THE OUTSIDE WALL OF THE THEATRE.

CLUE 3

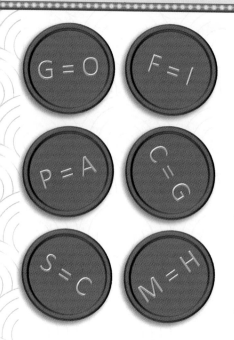

G = O

F = I

P = A

C = G

S = C

M = H

FIND TWO BADGES ON THE SIDE OF THE THEATRE,

TO MAKE THIS CRIME MORE CLEAR.

USE THE COINS ON THE LEFT, TO EXCHANGE THE LETTERS,

AND A 7-LETTER WORD WILL APPEAR.

ELIMINATE A THEATRE FROM YOUR LIST.

THIS AREA WAS ONCE LONDON'S NOTORIOUS RED-LIGHT DISTRICT, AS THE INFLUX OF PRETTY ACTRESSES PROVIDED AN ENDLESS FLOW OF GIRLS WHO WERE LOOKING TO SUPPLEMENT THEIR INCOMES. THERE WAS EVEN A DIRECTORY OF LOCAL PROSTITUTES KNOWN AS 'HARRIS'S LIST OF COVENT GARDEN LADIES' WHICH LISTED THE APPEARANCE, PRICE, AND SPECIALITIES OF THE OFFERINGS. ARGUABLY THE MOST FAMOUS SCANDAL THAT UNRAVELLED HERE WAS THE AFFAIR BETWEEN CHARLES II AND NELL GWYN, WHO HAD RISEN FROM A HUMBLE ORANGE SELLER TO THE FAVOURITE MISTRESS OF THE KING. AN UNDERGROUND TUNNEL RUNS FROM THE THEATRE TO THE NELL OF OLD DRURY PUB, WHICH WAS USED TO SNEAK AWAY FOR ROMANTIC LIAISONS BEFORE SLIPPING BACK FOR THE ROYAL APPLAUSE AT THE END OF THE SHOW.

STORY

The lives of Nell Gwyn and Molly May have some striking similarities. Both grew up around Drury Lane and hailed from humble working-class backgrounds. Both sold fruit to make a living, and they even shared the same star sign. Molly however did not get a chance encounter with a king, and her rise into the acting profession was a much harsher reality. Her parents refused to let her attend the theatre or join an acting group, so Molly was left to achieve her dream on her own.

DIRECTIONS

CONTINUE ALONG RUSSELL STREET, THEN TURN LEFT INTO DRURY LANE. TURN RIGHT AFTER THE PRINCE OF WALES PUB, AND FIND YOUR CLUE AT THE LARGE STONE BUILDING IN FRONT OF YOU.

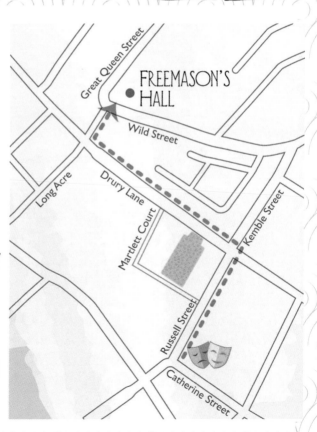

FIVE BRAVE FREEMASONS
LIE WITH THE SECRET,
OF EVERYTHING
YOU NEED TO KNOW.

USE THEIR FIRST NAME INITIALS,
TO FORM A 5-LETTER WORD,
WHICH WILL LINK YOU
TO A SHOW.

_____ FREYBER

_____ HALLOWE

_____ ROBINSON

_____ WILCO

_____ NELSO

ELIMINATE A SHOW FROM YOUR LIST.

STANDING BEFORE YOU IS THE GRAND LODGE OF THE FREEMASONS;
AN ANCIENT SOCIETY WHOSE MEMBERS FAMOUSLY GREET ONE
ANOTHER WITH A VARIETY OF SECRET HANDSHAKES BASED ON THEIR
RANK WITHIN THE ORGANISATION. THE SECRETIVE NATURE OF THE
FREEMASONS HAS LED TO MANY CONSPIRACY THEORIES, WITH SOME
BELIEVING THE MASONIC SYMBOL OF THE ALL-SEEING EYE, HIDDEN IN
PLAIN SIGHT ON AMERICAN $1 BANKNOTES, IS EVIDENCE THAT THEY
SECRETLY CONTROL THE WORLD. NOTABLE MEMBERS OVER THE
YEARS HAVE INCLUDED, CHARLES DARWIN, WINSTON CHURCHILL,
GEORGE WASHINGTON AND EVEN AMERICAN ASTRONAUT BUZZ
ALDRIN, WHO IN 1969 CONSECRATED A MASONIC LODGE ON
THE MOON.

STORY

Instead of following her dreams of stardom, Molly was forced to work on her father's fruit stand which was hard manual work for a young girl. The only thing she hated more than the early mornings and long days was seeing the privileged daughters of rich customers skipping by, who seemingly had life so easy. This early hardship lit a fire in Molly's belly to fight her way to the top, and her battle with the privileged elite stayed with her for life.

DIRECTIONS

RE-JOIN DRURY LANE, THEN TURN RIGHT. KEEP WALKING UNTIL YOU FIND THE WHITE HART PUB ON YOUR RIGHT.

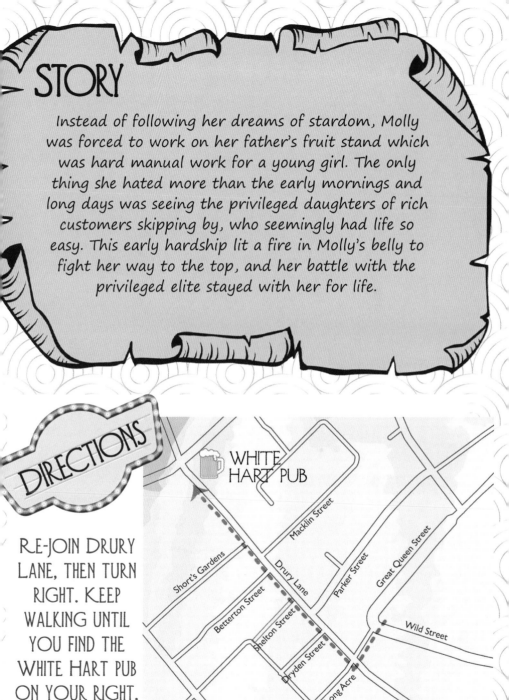

WHITE HART PUB

Macklin Street

Short's Gardens

Drury Lane

Parker Street

Great Queen Street

Betterton Street

Shelton Street

Wild Street

Dryden Street

Long Acre

CLUE 5

THIS
SURNAME
I
N
G

INSIDE THE PUB,
FIND A BOY WITH A FISH,
HE CAN HELP YOU SOLVE THIS CLUE.
SHOW HIM THIS PAGE,
AND LOOK OVER HIS SHOULDER,
AND ALL WILL BE REVEALED TO YOU.

ELIMINATE A SUSPECT FROM YOUR LIST.

THE WHITE HART CLAIMS TO BE LONDON'S OLDEST LICENCED ESTABLISHMENT, WHICH DATES BACK TO 1216.

IN THE 18TH CENTURY THIS PUB WAS NOTORIOUS FOR SERVING CONDEMNED MEN A FINAL DRINK BEFORE THEY FACED THE NOOSE, WHICH INCLUDED HIGHWAYMAN DICK TURPIN WHO DRANK HERE PRIOR TO HIS HANGING IN 1739. THE BUSY ROAD OUTSIDE (HIGH HOLBORN) IS BUILT ON THE FOUNDATIONS OF THE OLD ROMAN ROAD WHICH LINKED LONDON TO BATH AND WAS OFTEN TARGETED BY HIGHWAYMEN LOOKING TO ROB WEALTHY ARISTOCRATS.

STORY

When her shift on the fruit stand was finished, Molly worked nights at The White Hart, which was a great opportunity to mix with those connected to showbusiness. It was here that she developed a quick wit and sharp tongue; something that got her into trouble with other actresses later in life.

DIRECTIONS

CROSS THE ROAD AND JOIN HIGH HOLBORN. FOLLOW THE ROAD ROUND TO THE LEFT, AND INTO SHAFTESBURY AVENUE. THE ROAD BENDS TO THE LEFT TO BECOME MONMOUTH STREET. ON YOUR LEFT YOU WILL SEE A SMALL COVERED ALLEY THAT LEADS TO NEAL'S YARD. (JUST AFTER THE BLUE PLAQUE DEDICATED TO BRIAN EPSTEIN)

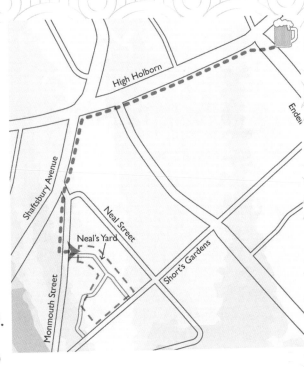

A MAN NAMED **MONTY** AND HIS **SNAKE**,
CAN BE FOUND WITHIN THIS YARD.
LOOK HIGH TO THE RIGHT,
FOR **TWO METAL THINGS**,
THAT LINK TO A THEATRE TO DISREGARD.

ELIMINATE A THEATRE FROM YOUR LIST.

THIS HIDDEN OASIS OF COLOUR TAKES ITS NAME FROM THOMAS NEALE, A PROMINENT POLITICIAN WHO FIRST DEVELOPED THE AREA WAY BACK IN 1690. JUST AROUND THE CORNER YOU'LL FIND THE LONDON OFFICE OF THE BEATLES' MANAGER BRIAN EPSTEIN. AFTER SEEING THEM PERFORM IN 1961, EPSTEIN IMMEDIATELY TOOK THE FAB FOUR UNDER HIS WING AND MASTERMINDED THEIR STRATOSPHERIC RISE TO SUPERSTARDOM, LEADING MANY TO DUB HIM 'THE FIFTH BEATLE'.
THIS YARD WAS ALSO ONCE HOME TO LEGENDARY COMEDY GROUP MONTY PYTHON, WHOSE FANS INCLUDED NONE OTHER THAN THE BEATLES' GEORGE HARRISON, WHO REMORTGAGED HIS OWN HOUSE TO FUND THEIR 1979 FILM LIFE OF BRIAN.

STORY

By the age of 19 Molly had saved enough of her own money to start paying for acting classes that took place above a butcher's shop in Neal's Yard. These classes were a mixed success. On the positive side, Molly was able to appear in some low-budget performances, and she discovered her love for singing and musical theatre. On the negative side, she was only offered small supporting roles, and eventually walked out in protest.

DIRECTIONS

CONTINUE THROUGH NEAL'S YARD AND EXIT ONTO SHORT'S GARDENS. TURN RIGHT, AND HEAD STRAIGHT TOWARDS A LARGE STONE MONUMENT IN THE MIDDLE OF THE ROAD, WHICH MARKS SEVEN DIALS.

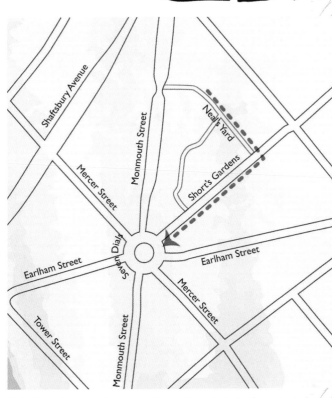

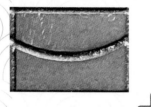 + 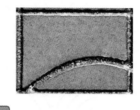 +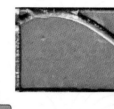

___ ___ ___

A **golden graph**,
hanging close to the column,
plots the movement of the sun.
Match the pieces to months,
then translate to a number,
and eliminate the total from page 1.

E.g.
January = 1
February = 2
March = 3
etc...

ELIMINATE A NUMBER FROM YOUR LIST.

STANDING IN THE CENTRE OF SEVEN DIALS, MANY WONDER WHY THE TOWERING MONUMENT IN FRONT OF YOU ONLY HAS 6 DIALS AT ITS BASE, BUT THIS IS BECAUSE THE COLUMN ITSELF ACTUALLY ACTS AS THE SEVENTH SUNDIAL. IN VICTORIAN TIMES THIS AREA WAS A NOTORIOUS SLUM, RIFE WITH PICKPOCKETS AND MURDERERS, AND INSPIRED THE SQUALID SCENES DESCRIBED IN SOME OF CHARLES DICKENS' MOST FAMOUS NOVELS. IT ALSO INSPIRED WILLIAM HOGARTH'S FAMOUS 'GIN LANE' DRAWING, WARNING OF THE PERILS OF DRUNKEN EXCESS. ACCORDING TO LEGEND, THE ORIGINAL COLUMN WAS TOPPLED BY A RIOTOUS MOB IN 1773 AS THEY HUNTED FOR TREASURE RUMOURED TO BE BURIED BENEATH.

Things were looking hopeless for Molly, until one afternoon a customer handed her a free ticket to the British Museum, which changed her life forever. It was here that she discovered the wonders of Ancient Egypt, and a heroine that she was born to play, Cleopatra. After months of hard work and countless auditions, she finally landed her dream role in the classic 'Antony and Cleopatra' at St. Martin's Theatre. Her performance was described as 'stunning' and the show ran for two months longer than scheduled. Molly's rise had begun.

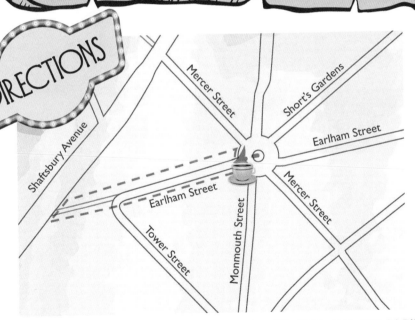

DIRECTIONS

FROM THE GRAPH, CROSS THE ROAD, AND HEAD TO THE RIGHT OF CAFFÉ NERO INTO EARLHAM STREET.

<u>PLEASE NOTE</u>: EARLHAM STREET RUNS IN TWO DIRECTIONS, MAKE SURE YOU HEAD SOUTH-WEST.

A WITNESS BY THE NAME OF 'COLLINS' CAN BE FOUND UP HIGH IN BLUE.

CROSS OUT ALL THE RED LETTERS, FOUND ON THE SIGN,

AND SIX WORDS WILL APPEAR TO YOU.

```
F B O O E Z Y
J A M Z Z L G
B A I N D F E
A G T F M A W
C H U M R C H
```

ELIMINATE A SHOW FROM YOUR LIST.

WHEN THE MOUSETRAP FIRST OPENED ITS DOORS WAY BACK IN 1952, ITS WRITER AGATHA CHRISTIE THOUGHT IT WOULD RUN FOR 8 MONTHS AT MOST. HOWEVER, ALL THESE YEARS LATER THIS LEGENDARY PLAY IS STILL GOING STRONG, MAKING IT THE WORLD'S LONGEST RUNNING PRODUCTION. IN 1959 A SPECIAL PERFORMANCE OF THIS FAMOUS MURDER MYSTERY WAS GIVEN AT WORMWOOD SCRUBS PRISON, LEAVING OFFICERS WITH A MYSTERY OF THEIR OWN TO SOLVE AFTER TWO PRISONERS ESCAPED DURING THE SHOW. AS WELL AS HOLDING THE RECORD FOR THE LONGEST RUNNING PRODUCTION, CHRISTIE IS ALSO THE BEST SELLING NOVELIST IN HISTORY, HAVING SOLD A STAGGERING 2 BILLION BOOKS WORLDWIDE.

STORY

After Molly's huge success as Cleopatra, she was determined to join a famous drama academy in Earlham Street, but her limited acting experience, low social status and lack of money prevented her from ever gaining membership. This was further fuel to the fire, making Molly even more resentful of the privileged actresses around her. Molly knew that if she was going to make it to the top, she would have to do it on her own, so instead focussed on networking among London's showbiz elite.

DIRECTIONS

AT THE END OF EARLHAM STREET TURN LEFT INTO TOWER STREET, THEN TAKE A RIGHT INTO TOWER COURT, WHICH RUNS ALONGSIDE ST MARTIN'S THEATRE. YOU EMERGE OPPOSITE THE IVY.

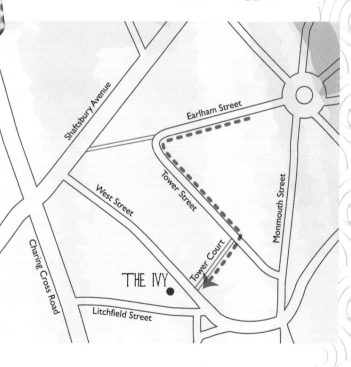

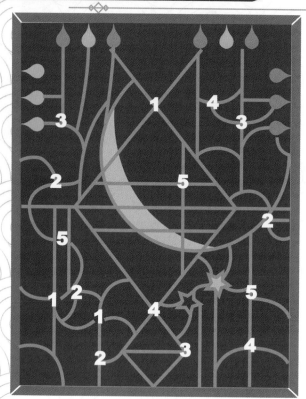

THE IVY RESTAURANT'S FAMOUS WINDOW, HOLDS A RATHER MYSTERIOUS TWIST.

MATCH THE **WHITE DIAMONDS** TO NUMBERS, AND ADD THEM TOGETHER TO ELIMINATE A NUMBER FROM YOUR LIST.

ELIMINATE A NUMBER

SITTING IN THE HEART OF LONDON'S FAMOUS THEATRE DISTRICT, THIS WORLD RENOWNED RESTAURANT WAS FIRST OPENED IN 1917 AND BEGAN LIFE AS A SMALL ITALIAN CAFÉ WITHOUT EVEN AN ALCOHOL LICENCE. HOWEVER, FROM ITS HUMBLE BEGINNINGS IT QUICKLY GREW TO BECOME THE GO-TO PLACE FOR ANYONE WHO WAS ANYONE IN THEATRE LAND. OVER THE YEARS THE IVY HAS ENTERTAINED A LONG LIST OF CELEBRITY STARS, FROM NOEL COWARD AND LAURENCE OLIVIER, TO TOM CRUISE AND ANGELINA JOLIE. IN THE EARLY YEARS IT WOULD EVEN HAND DELIVER MEALS DIRECTLY TO THE STARS' DRESSING ROOMS IN BETWEEN SHOWS.

STORY

Molly knew that if she was going to mix with the elite of the theatre world, there was only one place to go; London's Ivy Restaurant. It was here that the biggest names would have lunch and sign big-money contracts, and where Molly spent 3-months savings on one meal, on the off chance of a lucky break. A jealous co-star later claimed that Molly became involved in a scandalous affair with a married theatre producer after meeting in the Ivy that night, but whatever the reason, acting work began pouring in.

DIRECTIONS

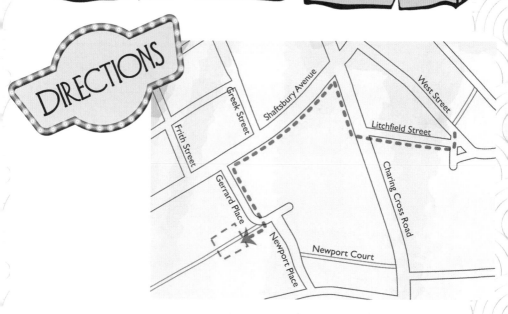

JOIN LITCHFIELD STREET, THEN TURN RIGHT, AND LEFT ALONG SHAFTESBURY AVENUE. TURN LEFT INTO GERRARD PLACE AND INTO CHINATOWN. YOUR CLUE CAN BE FOUND AT THE TOP OF THE FIRST CHINESE GATE THAT YOU COME ACROSS.

FIND 4 SYMBOLS, <u>AT THE TOP</u>, OF <u>EACH SIDE</u> OF THE GATE,
THEN ELIMINATE A SUSPECT WITH THE TWO WORDS YOU CREATE..

<u>ELIMINATE A SUSPECT</u> FROM YOUR LIST.

LONDON'S ORIGINAL 'CHINATOWN' WAS LOCATED IN THE EAST END,
AND FEATURED AN ARRAY OF GAMBLING AND OPIUM DENS THAT
CATERED FOR CHINESE SAILORS WHO WERE CONCENTRATED THERE.
THIS WEST END VERSION WAS OPENED IN THE 1970S. GERRARD
STREET ITSELF WAS ORIGINALLY BUILT BETWEEN 1677 AND 1685 AND
BY THE MID-18TH CENTURY, HAD BECOME WELL-KNOWN FOR ITS VAST
ARRAY OF COFFEE HOUSES AND TAVERNS WHICH WERE FREQUENTED
BY LITERARY FIGURES OF THE TIME. THIS STREET ALSO FEATURES IN THE
FAMOUS CHARLES DICKENS NOVEL 'GREAT EXPECTATIONS' AS THE
HOME OF PIP'S GUARDIAN MR JAGGERS.

STORY

Molly was now becoming a familiar face on London's theatre scene, and in 1919 appeared on the front cover of the city's leading showbiz magazine under the headline 'a rising star'. She could also now afford to rent an expensive flat in Shaftesbury Avenue, which was right in the heart of Theatreland and close to all of the lively parties that she regularly attended. Despite her growing success, Molly was still looked down upon by more privileged actresses, who became increasingly jealous of her rising fame. And there was one girl in particular who was a particular nemesis of hers...

DIRECTIONS

GO THE END OF GERRARD STREET AND TURN RIGHT.

KEEP WALKING, THEN ENTER ST ANNE'S CHURCHYARD. YOUR CLUE IS ON THE OUTSIDE WALL OF THE CHURCH.

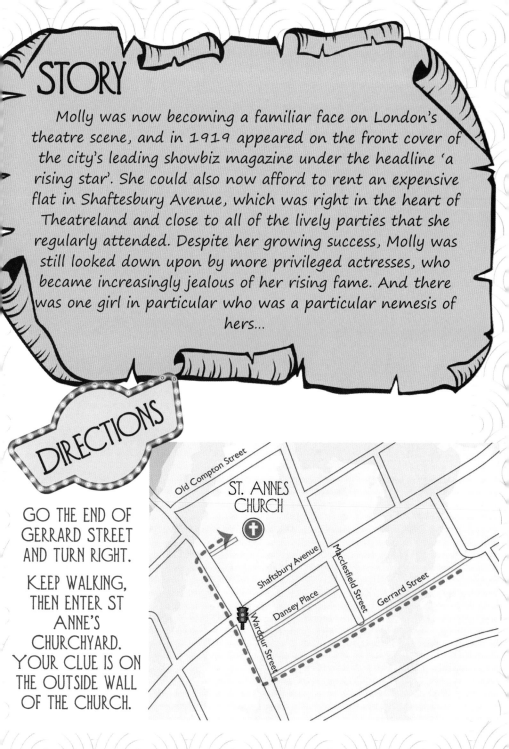

CLUE 11

BENEATH THE
KING OF CORSICA,
ARE FIVE ROLES
IN A POEM,

BUT IN THE LIST
UPON THE RIGHT,
THERE IS ONE
EXTRA SHOWING.

CAST LIST:

- HERO
- SLAVE
- TEACHER
- KING
- CARPENTER
- BEGGAR

ELIMINATE A SUSPECT LINKED TO THAT EXTRA ROLE.

DATING BACK TO THE 1600S, THE HISTORIC CHURCHYARD OF ST ANNE'S VISIBLY RISES 6 FT ABOVE THE PAVEMENT DUE TO THE ESTIMATE 13,000 BURIALS WITHIN. IN THE EARLY 20TH CENTURY THIS STREET WAS AT THE CENTRE OF A BRITISH FILM MAKING CRAZE, LEADING MANY TO NICKNAME IT 'FILM ROW'. NO FEWER THAN 20 FILM COMPANIES WERE ONCE BASED HERE, INCLUDING BRITISH PATHE AND WARNER BROTHERS. AWAY FROM THE BIG SCREEN, IN 1926 ON NEARBY FRITH STREET, LEGENDARY SCOTTISH INVENTOR JOHN LOGIE BAIRD UNVEILED THE FIRST EVER TELEVISION. STARTING LIFE AS A RUDIMENTARY PROTOTYPE COBBLED TOGETHER WITH AN OLD HAT BOX, A SET OF BICYCLE LIGHTS, SOME SEWING NEEDLES AND A PAIR OF SCISSORS, BAIRD'S INVENTION WOULD LATER GO ON TO CHANGE THE WORLD.

STORY

Climbing the slippery showbiz ladder alongside Molly was another young actress, who she saw as her arch enemy. This actress was from a privileged background, went to the city's finest drama academy, and was often competing at the same auditions. After repeatedly missing out on roles, this actress began to gossip about Molly, creating scandalous stories about her past. With wild stories flying around about her, work began to dry up, and Molly believed this actress had ruined her chances of getting her big break.

DIRECTIONS

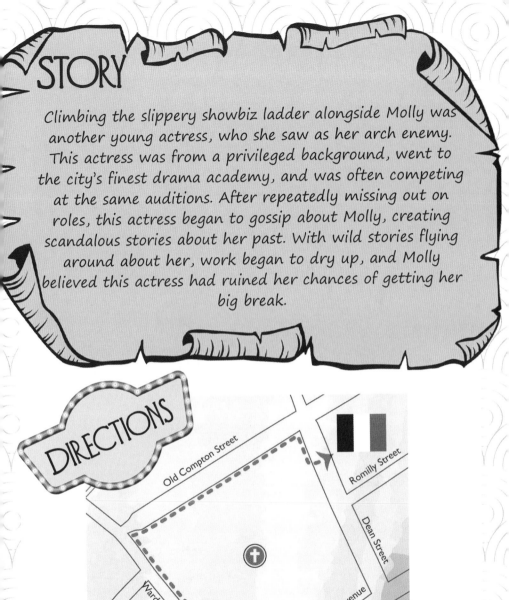

RETURN TO WARDOUR STREET AND TURN RIGHT, THEN TAKE THE FIRST RIGHT INTO OLD COMPTON STREET. TURN RIGHT INTO DEAN STREET AND THEN ENTER THE FRENCH HOUSE PUB.

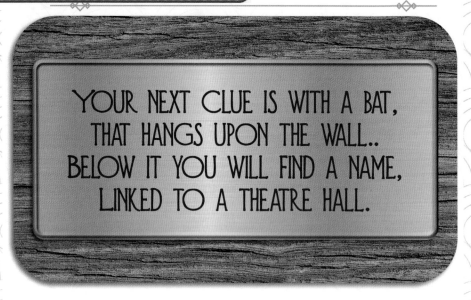

THE FRENCH HOUSE

CLUE 12

YOUR NEXT CLUE IS WITH A BAT,
THAT HANGS UPON THE WALL..
BELOW IT YOU WILL FIND A NAME,
LINKED TO A THEATRE HALL.

ELIMINATE A THEATRE FROM YOUR LIST.

THE FRENCH HOUSE IS FAMOUS FOR A PECULIAR TRADITION; IT ONLY EVER SERVES BEER BY HALF MEASURES, EXCEPT ON APRIL 1ST WHEN A CELEBRITY IS INVITED TO POUR ITS ONLY ANNUAL PINT, WHICH IS THEN AUCTIONED FOR CHARITY. IN 1940 THIS BAR HAD A RATHER FAMOUS REGULAR, THE EXILED FRENCH PRESIDENT CHARLES DE GAULLE. THIS VENUE BECAME THE UNOFFICIAL HEADQUARTERS FOR HIS 'FREE FRENCH' MOVEMENT AND LEGEND HAS IT THAT IT WAS IN AN UPSTAIRS ROOM THAT HE DRAFTED HIS FAMOUS SPEECH "À TOUS LES FRANÇAIS", CALLING FOR FRENCH RESISTANCE TO GERMAN OCCUPATION.

STORY

It was here in 1920 that the feud between Molly May and her arch enemy spilled over, in a scandalous brawl that made it into the city's papers. After enjoying several glasses of champagne, her rival actress strolled into the bar with her arm around the very same theatre producer who allegedly gave Molly her showbiz break, and taunted her about her stalling career. Molly pushed her to the ground, and was dragged away by police, as her rival shouted that she would get her revenge.

DIRECTIONS

EXIT THE FRENCH HOUSE AND TURN RIGHT, THEN TAKE THE FIRST RIGHT INTO OLD COMPTON STREET.

TURN LEFT ON GREEK STREET, WHICH IS THE LOCATION OF YOUR NEXT CLUE.

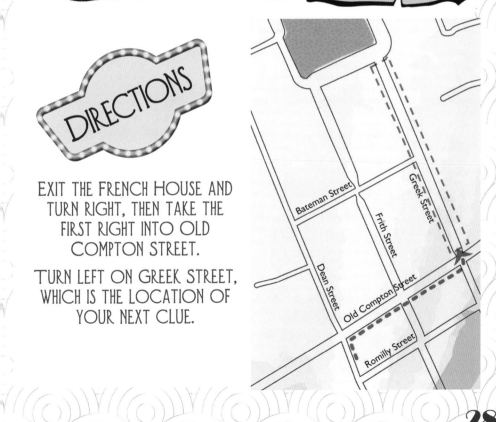

LOOK UP HIGH TO FIND YOUR CLUE, MARKED BY A MAN BETWEEN PILLARS OF BLUE

ELIMINATE A THEATRE FROM YOUR LIST.

THIS STREET WAS ONCE HOME TO THE SHOWROOM OF LEGENDARY ENTREPRENEUR JOSIAH WEDGWOOD, OTHERWISE KNOWN AS THE 'FATHER OF ENGLISH POTTERS'. FOUNDED IN 1759, THE WEDGWOOD COMPANY QUICKLY EARNED A REPUTATION FOR ITS LUXURY CERAMICS WHICH ONCE GRACED THE TABLES OF QUEEN CHARLOTTE, THE WHITE HOUSE AND EVEN THE VATICAN. WEDGWOOD WAS ALSO THE PIONEER OF MANY OF THE SALES TECHNIQUES WE RECOGNISE TODAY, INCLUDING ILLUSTRATED CATALOGUES, CELEBRITY ENDORSEMENTS AND EVEN BUY ONE GET ONE FREE OFFERS. THE FAMILY FLAIR FOR REVOLUTIONARY THINKING DIDN'T STOP WITH JOSIAH HOWEVER... HIS GRANDSON CHARLES DARWIN FAMOUSLY WENT ON TO DEVELOP THE THEORY OF EVOLUTION!

STORY

While Molly sat in a coffee house in Greek Street, despairing at her stalled career, one of London's most famous theatre producers walked in by chance, with the opportunity of a lifetime. Cecil Taylor-Davies was working on a new high-budget musical 'The Lady of the Rose', but his lead actress had just fallen pregnant. Desperate for a replacement, Molly was given the shot she had always dreamed of, and in an amazing stroke of luck, was offered the role of Leading Lady in his major new show. This was Molly's big break.

CONTINUE ALONG GREEK STREET, THEN FIND YOUR NEXT CLUE SOMEWHERE ALONG THE EAST SIDE OF SOHO SQUARE.

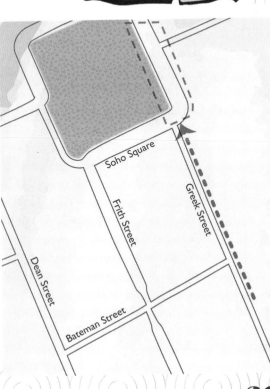

BELOW A PAIR OF **OLD CROSSED KEYS**,
IS A **LATIN INSCRIPTION** IN STONE.
COUNT THE NUMBER OF TIMES EACH LETTER APPEARS,
AND REMOVE THE **TOTAL** FROM PAGE ONE.

__ __ __ __ __ __ __

S T A I R S

ELIMINATE A NUMBER FROM YOUR LIST.

THE DUKE OF MONMOUTH, BASTARD SON OF CHARLES II, ONCE LIVED
IN THIS SQUARE. HE FAMOUSLY TRIED TO SEIZE THE THRONE AFTER HIS
FATHER'S DEATH, AND WAS DEFEATED AT THE BATTLE OF SEDGEMOOR.
AFTER THE BATTLE, THE DUKE WAS ARRESTED AND BEHEADED ON TOWER
HILL, HOWEVER WHEN THEY BROUGHT HIS HEADLESS CORPSE TO THE
TOWER OF LONDON, AUTHORITIES REALISED THAT THEY HAD NO
OFFICIAL PORTRAIT OF HIM. HIS HEAD WAS HASTILY STITCHED BACK ON
BY A SURGEON (COVERING THE WOUND WITH A CRAVAT) AND A
PORTRAIT WAS QUICKLY COMPLETED BEFORE THE BODY DECOMPOSED.
THAT PAINTING IS NOW ON DISPLAY A SHORT WALK FROM THIS SQUARE,
IN THE NATIONAL PORTRAIT GALLERY.

STORY

The production of 'The Lady of the Rose' was scheduled to premiere at The Soho Theatre on 1st July 1921, replacing the longstanding hit musical 'Show Boat' that had been entertaining audiences for years. The pressure was on for Molly to deliver, as the eyes of the theatre world would be scrutinising her every move. But just one week before the opening night, disaster struck. Molly's supporting actress pulled out due to illness and was replaced by none other than her bitter arch rival. Things quickly began to fall apart.

DIRECTIONS

HEAD ACROSS SOHO SQUARE, AND ENTER CARLISLE STREET.

TAKE THE FIRST LEFT, THEN FIRST RIGHT, INTO ST ANNE'S COURT, WHICH IS THE LOCATION OF YOUR NEXT CLUE.

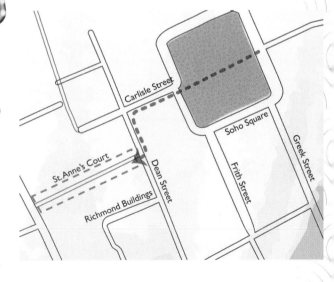

AN OLD WHITE SIGN MARKS
CLARION HOUSE,
ONCE THE HOME OF
REFUGEES.
THEY CAME TO LONDON
FROM **TWO** MAIN
COUNTRIES,
MATCH THE SUSPECT'S
INITIALS TO THESE.

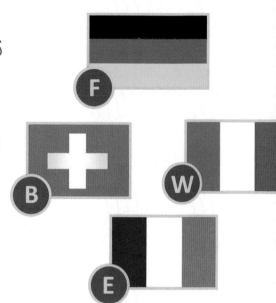

ELIMINATE A SUSPECT FROM YOUR LIST.

AS YOU CONTINUE DOWN THIS ALLEY, YOU WILL FIND A BLUE PLAQUE MARKING THE LEGENDARY 'TRIDENT STUDIOS' WHICH IS WHERE SOME OF THE MOST ICONIC SONGS OF THE 20TH CENTURY WERE RECORDED, INCLUDING DAVID BOWIE'S 'ZIGGY STARDUST' AND 'HEY JUDE' BY THE BEATLES. OTHER FAMOUS NAMES TO HAVE ONCE RECORDED HERE INCLUDE THE BEE GEES, ELTON JOHN, QUEEN AND THE ROLLING STONES, TO NAME BUT A FEW. SOHO HAS MORE THAN ONE CLAIM TO MUSICAL FAME THOUGH, AS IN NEARBY FRITH STREET AN 8-YEAR-OLD PRODIGY BY THE NAME OF WOLFGANG AMADEUS MOZART COMPOSED SOME OF HIS EARLIEST WORKS, OPPOSITE WHAT IS NOW RONNIE SCOTT'S JAZZ CLUB.

STORY

Despite all of her hard work and dreams of perfection, Molly's opening night was a complete disaster. Props fell over, dancers tripped, and lighting failed; all of which Molly believed were deliberate acts of sabotage by her rival to destroy her big moment. At the end of this disastrous night, Molly stormed out of the theatre, and in the blink of an eye, tumbled down the stairs in front of the waiting paparazzi. As crowds gathered Molly screamed out that she'd been pushed, but nobody saw what happened.

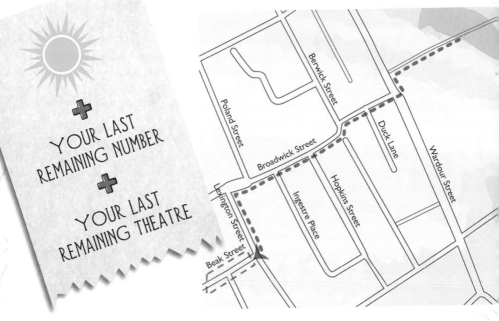

✚
YOUR LAST
REMAINING NUMBER
✚
YOUR LAST
REMAINING THEATRE

USE YOUR LAST REMAINING NUMBER & THEATRE ON PAGE 1 TO FIND THE LOCATION OF YOUR FINAL CLUE SOMEWHERE IN BEAK STREET. THE CLUE IS SOMEWHERE **INSIDE** THAT LOCATION.

YOUR FINAL CLUE
APPEARS ON **FILM**,
YOU'VE NEARLY
CRACKED THIS **CASE**.
SAT BENEATH, A 'CROSS OF IRON',
A WEST END SHOW AWAITS.

ELIMINATE THIS SHOW FROM YOUR LIST.

SOHO WAS ONCE RENOWNED FOR THE LARGE COMMUNITY OF SWISS WATCHMAKERS WHO PLIED THEIR TRADE HERE... SO MUCH SO THAT MANY DESCRIBED THIS AREA AS THE 13TH COUNTY (CANTON) OF SWITZERLAND, WHICH IS THE ORIGIN OF THE PUB'S CURIOUS NAME. PERHAPS THE FIRST NAME THAT SPRINGS TO MIND WHEN YOU THINK OF LUXURY SWISS WATCHES IS ROLEX, HOWEVER, THEY WERE ACTUALLY FOUNDED HERE IN LONDON, AND DIDN'T MOVE TO SWITZERLAND UNTIL 1919. PAINSTAKINGLY HANDCRAFTED AND TAKING A YEAR TO MAKE, ROLEXES ARE AMONG THE WORLD'S MOST SOUGHT AFTER TIMEPIECES, AND IN 2017 A NEW WORLD RECORD WAS SET WHEN PAUL NEWMAN'S RARE 'ROLEX DAYTONA' SOLD AT AUCTION FOR A WHOPPING $17.7 MILLION.

STORY

Following the incident on the stairs, one eyewitness said that the actress playing the 'Flower Girl' had started a heated argument in the interval, after telling Molly that she 'belonged on a fruit stand, not a West End stage'. According to the witness, 'Those two have hated each other for years, and this was just the tip of the iceberg'. Despite these claims, nobody saw her push Molly, and so the charges were dropped. As there was no understudy, 'The Lady of the Rose' could no longer run, and was cancelled after just one night. But what was the fate of the two leading ladies?...

THE FINAL REVEAL...

THE LAST REMAINING INFO,
YOU HAVE UPON **PAGE 1**,
WILL TELL YOU THE **THEATRE**
AND THE **SHOW**,
STARRING THE GUILTY ONE.
FIND YOUR SUSPECT IN THIS PUB,
AND IT WILL ALL MAKE SENSE,
YOU'LL FIND HER WHERE SHE LOVED TO BE,
STANDING IN FRONT OF LADIES AND GENTS.

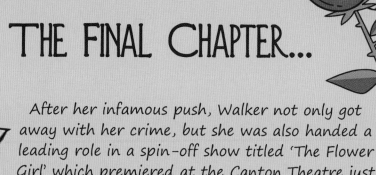

THE FINAL CHAPTER....

After her infamous push, Walker not only got away with her crime, but she was also handed a leading role in a spin-off show titled 'The Flower Girl' which premiered at the Canton Theatre just a year later. But this was where her luck turned. The musical was a huge flop, and Walker's fortunes quickly dwindled. Unable to secure any acting roles, she was forced to look for other work, and in an ironic twist of fate, spent the latter years of her life selling roses on the London Underground.

As for Molly, she had the last laugh. After spending five years out of the public eye, she reappeared in 1927 as a street performer in Covent Garden, with a brilliant new comedy about a clumsy apple seller called Mrs Smith. 'The Apple Lady' won countless awards, made her a small fortune, and became one of London's most adored characters; so much so, that she became forever immortalised when a new type of apple arrived in the country in the 1930s and was named in her honour, the 'Granny Smith'.